WHAT YOU SAY, YOU DO

LO QUE SE DICE, SE HACE

JOSÉ MEDINA

VELÁZQUEZ PRESS

Velázquez Press
9682 Telstar Ave., Ste. 110
El Monte, CA 91731 USA
www.VelazquezPress.com

ISBN 10: 1-59495-751-7
ISBN 13: 978-1-59495-751-2

Printed in China by Global PSD

First Edition

23 22 21 20 19   1 2 3 4 5

Library of Congress Control Number: In Progress

To my family:

Thank you for believing in me, even when I could not see the light.

To my abuelita Juanita:

"Lo que se dice, se hace" is a part of me, today and always.

Introduction

Everyone has a story. There are things that happen in our lives that shape the person we become. Some people call these stories, testimonies, or *testimonios* in Spanish. This is my *testimonio*.

In the following poems, I share with you, the reader, what happened in my life between the ages of five and seven. It was a traumatic time for me. As the first son of immigrant parents from Mexico, I did not speak any English when I started school in El Paso, Texas. In the mid-1970s, much like today in many places, it was a bad thing if you did not speak English in U.S. schools.

I decided to write about my *testimonio* because now, as an educational leader and former school principal, I see that my story is not that different from what others continue to experience today. The setting may not be the same, but the feelings of not belonging to any one culture, the fear of speaking Spanish because some might not like it, having others see you as an immigrant in your own land... that unfortunately, has not changed.

It is my hope that by sharing my *testimonio*, others will be willing to do the same. Only when we bring to light the experiences as students who were forced to lose our language and culture in the name of the "American dream," can we begin to heal, own who we are, share our given names, and continue to inspire others to do the same.

Back to School Night:
Part One

I stand.

I am lost in my past.

Hundreds of students and their families stare at me,
as I nervously hold the microphone in my hand.

"*Gracias por estar con nosotros esta tarde.* We are so excited that you were able to make it to our first ever Back to School Night. How lucky are we that we get to open this new school together? I am the school principal. *Mi nombre es* José Luis Medina Hernández Franco López Jr. Díaz-Cruz!"

The room bursts with laughter!

I can breathe again.

"I never dreamed that I would be a school principal."

Mi mamá,

Mi papá,

My entire family is here to experience this.

My parents sit in the front row, their pride palpable. For, you see, as their first born, I have carried their dreams and hopes on my shoulders for as long as I can remember.

Blessed. *¡Qué bendición!*

"I want you to know that I am so grateful that you have decided to trust us—to trust me, with your children's education."

I feel a knot in my throat.

I am about to cry in front of the entire group.

You see, they don't understand yet that my journey to this place,
to this cafeteria stage, has been a long one.

The Best First Day of Kindergarten

I am five years old and excited to go to Monte Vista Elementary School!

It will be the best first day of kindergarten ever!

Mi mamá y mi papá have taken me to downtown El Paso to buy new school clothes.

I look *guapo*.

I am wearing brown slacks and a white button-down shirt.

And, brown shoes from *Los Tres Hermanos,* the best shoe store in *Juárez*!

> I am holding my parents' hands and I see the
> school and I begin to feel sick and I am
> sweaty and I want to
> go back home so that I can speak *español*
> to my *abuelita* Juanita
> who told me that she would love me more
> if I did well in school and I
> want to make sure that I am a good boy because
> I am smart and I don't speak
> English because my parents don't
> know how to speak English and I want to
> go home
> go home
> go home
> go home.

It wasn't the best first day of kinder because I am stupid.
It wasn't the best first day of kinder because I peed in my pants.
It wasn't the best first day of kinder because I ran from the teacher.
And I ran from my parents
And I kicked the teacher
And I bit my *papá*.

It wasn't the best second day of kinder because I did it all again.
It wasn't the best fifth day of kinder because I did it all again.
It wasn't the best ninth day of kinder because I did it all again.

It was never the best day of kinder because the principal told my parents I couldn't go back to Monte Vista Elementary School until I was six.

When I was six, I did it all over again.

I still can't speak English.

La Lotería

"La sirena."

"El alacrán."

"La dama."

"La calavera."

"¡Buenas! ¡Lotería!"

When I was five, I loved Saturdays!

Mis primas, who were from Durango, but now lived with us on weekends, came to the house on Saturdays.

During the week they worked in houses, cleaning them, but on Saturdays, they came to our house on Missouri Drive.

All of them had crossed the river to come and work in El Paso and they saved me because on Saturdays, we played *Lotería*.

Because there was drinks and *botana,* my
parents would forget about my not staying in school
and would not be as mad at me especially
because I was doing good with my learning
to read in *español* because my *mamá* was
mad that I was not in kinder and
so, I had to learn to read at home *con el
pellizco*, the pinch, which hurt but I didn't
care because at least my parents still loved me.

There was laughter, and screaming, and music, and I loved Saturdays because I was free.

I was a kid with a mission.

To win as many dollars as possible.

One quarter for the *lotería*, one quarter for the *esquinas*, one quarter for the *centro*, and one quarter for the *llena.*

On Saturdays, I was five. On Saturdays, it didn't matter that I was kicked out of kinder. On Saturdays, I was the *lotería* king.

Abuelita Juanita's Favorite

My *mamá* had gone to start looking for a job again because I promised I would stay in school when I was six and in first grade.

She went to Levi's and also, to Farah—to see who would hire her to sew the pants that people bought in the stores.

La mamá de mi mamá was named Juanita.
She loved me.
But, she was tough.
I was her favorite even though I did not speak English and I got kicked out of kindergarten.
She didn't tell anyone that I was her favorite, but she told me that I was her favorite one time when we were watching television.

When I didn't obey her, she would scream *como loca*!

She would grab one of her *chanclas*, not the ones with heels, but the plastic ones that were so worn out that they were hard, you know which ones?

Juanita would chase me *gritando, "¡Junior, te voy a pegar!"*

She did.

But, she would always hug me after she gave me the *chanclazo* and hold me in her arms. She would say, *"Junior, lo que se dice, se hace. Si dices que vas a hacer algo, lo tienes que hacer— si no, no eres persona de tu palabra."*

It meant a lot to me. Being in her arms. Juanita telling me that I had to do what I said I was going to do—or else, my words meant nothing.

I loved Juanita. I love Juanita. I was her favorite even though I did not speak English and I got kicked out of kindergarten.

Western Playland

For Easter, we always went to Western Playland at *Ascárate* Park.

My favorite ride, even at five, was *Los Huevitos.*

It was a ride with these little eggs that you jumped into and held on and they went in circles, and circles, and circles, and circles.

My *papá* had to get on with me because my *mamá* got scared and dizzy, and she cried when she was scared and dizzy.

My brother Gilberto, who was three years younger, couldn't get on because he was little.

He liked Western Playland too, but he could only get on the rides for babies.

Even when I skipped kindergarten, I got to go to Western Playland because it was on Easter, and Easter was important, and we went to church, and dressed nicely, and we went to Western Playland.

My Sixth Birthday

My godmother Lupe was mad that I
was not staying in school at Monte Vista Elementary School, and she
was even more angry that I got kicked out of kindergarten and
that I did not speak English like her daughters,
who were my cousins, but
they were older and not young like me.

My godmother Lupe was mad that I
was *un niño mal criado*, because I didn't behave and was a bad
child, and so, she told my parents that they
should have my sixth birthday party without me,
but I didn't know, and so I got to pick out my *piñata*, and
I helped to fill the bags for guests with *dulces* because I was going
to be six and not five, and when I got dressed,
my *papá* who was young and listened to my
godmother Lupe told me that we were going to the
store to pick up more things, but it was a lie because
we drove to her house in the
Segundo Barrio neighborhood, and my *papá*
was crying when he carried me screaming and
wailing because I found out that I was not
going to my sixth birthday party
because I did not stay in school, and this was
what they needed to do so that I would stay
in first grade when school began in September.

I saw my *papá* walk away sad, and confused, and with tears in his eyes as I cried, and
cried, and cried because it was my birthday party and I wanted to go.

My cousin Angelita later told me it was a good party.

Ciudad Juárez

Some weekends, we would take my Abuelita Juanita to her house in Juárez.

Every Sunday, there was a house full of *primos* and *primas*.

My cousins from my Tío Chava, and
my Tío Fernan*do*, and my Tío
Agustín, and we would all be there
having fun every Sunday because my
abuelita had bought a record player, and
we would put on the records that my
parents had bought for us in La Casa de
Música de Lux where everyone bought
their records, and the record
player was tall with a box that had flashing lights on the front
like if you were in a discotheque, and we loved
to dance so that we all imagined we were
grown-ups dancing to disco, and *rancheras*, and *cumbias*
too, and we
danced and danced until
it was time to go outside and play
mamaleche.

St. Joseph's School

I am six years old and I have already been kicked out of kindergarten...
and first grade.

Urine stained pants,
screaming and crying,
kicking teachers,
running out classrooms
and into the streets that would take me away from this school,
this torture.

These were my offenses and as such, I had to suffer the consequences.

Being a nervous child who did not speak English
was not an excuse.

Margarita and José Luis, my parents, are very young
very young
very young
and
they have tried everything
to make me
stay in school
they have brought me here
to St. Joseph's
where I will finally
learn my lesson
learn to stay in school
learn to become an American student
because an American student
is what I have to be
to be an American student
is why they left *México*
for a better future
for me
for me to have a better future
the principal
asks the nurse
to bring in
the
gurney
the
gurney
the
gurney

from the nurse's office
and
the principal
tells my parents
who
don't speak
English
who
speak
a beautiful language
español
but it doesn't matter here
because they don't
speak that language here
because only English
matters
it's what I need to know now
but I don't
because my *mamá*
only taught me
how to read and write
in *español*
and that does not
count
it doesn't
count
at all
the principal
tells my parents
to hold me down
so that they can strap
me
down to the rolling bed
and I begin to shout
to scream
I am going to learn
English
because I am an American student
but the straps feel tight around
my chest
and my arms
and my legs
and I need to learn how to
be an
American student
because that is the
dream

because this is the
school where I will learn
English
this is my punishment
for peeing in my pants
for running out of class
for kicking the teachers
for getting kicked out of kindergarten
for getting kicked out of first grade
and this
is my punishment because
I deserve this
because I am bad
and I don't speak
English.

The straps feel tight around
my chest
and my arms
and my legs.

I see my *mamá* and my *papá*.

Their tears screaming for help in a language they do not speak.

Their elementary education from Ciudad Juárez did not prepare them for this.

The gurney is rolled into my first-grade classroom.

My new teacher, Ms. McDow, speaks.

"Class, we have a new student. His name is Joe."

Laying in a puddle of my own urine,
bound by two straps,
my name no longer José,
I watch it all,
as if from above.

Back to School Night:
Part Two

I am so excited that my *mamá* and my *papá* are here to see how much I have learned from them.

I need them to know that they are the reason why my brother Gilberto, my sister Vanessa...
>	why the three of us are so proud of who they are,
>	where we come from,
>	and of our beautiful *español*.

My parents need to realize that because of their struggles,
>	we work hard for ourselves and for those we serve,
>	and ultimately,
>	it is why the three of us love and respect them so much.

I ask my family to join me on stage.

"I want to introduce you to my family. *Mi hermosa familia.* Along with all of my students, and you, they are the reason why I wake up each morning ready to disrupt a school system that has often taken away our language and culture."

As I look into the audience, most of the students and parents look like me.

They look like my parents, José Luis and Margarita, so many years earlier, dreaming of a
better
future
for their children.

These families—their hopes and dreams, yet to become a reality.

This is our purpose.

This is why this school community will be different.

This is why every experience in my life has brought me to this moment.

"The only person who could not be here today is my Abuelita Juanita. She lives in Juárez and planned to be here, but she is 90 years old and was not feeling well. *Estaba malita.* But, don't worry. I will tell you about Juanita soon. *Ella está* everywhere!"

My First Friend

Patrick was the first boy who became my friend at St. Joseph's.

He was smart, and all of the boys liked to play with him.

But, Patrick liked to play with me.

He only spoke English and I only spoke *español*.

I was excited that I got to play with him during recess.

Patrick would chase me around the playground like if he was trying to scare me and I just laughed and ran away.

Every day, we played the same game.

Patrick taught me one of the first words I learned in English.

"Wetback! Joe, you are a wetback! Wetback! Wetback! Wetback!"

I was glad someone wanted to play with me.

"Siempre en Domingo"

Juan Gabriel was my favorite singer in the world!

His songs touched *mi corazón* and I loved to sing along.

I remember when I first saw him.

Raúl Velasco was the host of the Sunday variety show, *Siempre en Domingo*, that every Mexican AND Mexican-American watched.

Raúl announced that Juan Gabriel was making a special appearance, which was rare because the singer preferred to sing on cassette tapes and in concert—not on television.

As I watched him *cantando* on the television screen, I felt *alegría*.

I was so proud that I spoke *español* and that I could understand every word he sang because it was like he was touching my heart.

Siempre en Domingo gave me many gifts:
the love of Juan Gabriel;
the love of *música en español*;
the love for the language that made me, me.

And, now that I stayed in first grade and no longer ran away from school, I could enjoy *Siempre en Domingo* every week!

Napkin

Ms. McDow was my first-grade teacher and
she was the one that
decided that my name was Joe and not
José
because I needed to learn English and
not speak *español* in class because
we were in the United States and I needed
to be an American because that
is why, I came to school.

I remember her laugh because she
laughed in threes—
Ha! Pause.
Ha! Pause.
Ha! Pause.

Ms. McDow was reading a book
to us and we were sitting
on the carpet, and I really
liked listening to her
read because she was my
teacher, and I wanted to be
a good student because a
good student is what my parents wanted, and they would tell me,
"pórtate bien."

And, so I tried to listen to them, and I behaved.

The book was about a picnic and there
was a picnic basket,
but some ants
got into the picnic basket, and also
there were
forks, and
spoons, and
knives
mentioned
in the
book,
and a
napkin.

I raised my hand because
my teacher said
that if we didn't
know a word that we should raise our hand, and so,
I raised my hand because I didn't know the word
napkin.

Several of the students started to laugh, including my
best friend Patrick, and
my face felt hot because
I didn't know English and I didn't know
napkin,
and I should know
napkin,
because others
were laughing, and
napkin
is a word I should know because
I needed to speak
English
so that I could be
American,
because American
was good and Mexican
was not good, and
now, I stayed in school,
and I didn't run away, and
napkin
was a word that I needed
to know to be
American
and a good student.

Ms. McDow laughed.

"You don't know the word napkin, Joe?"

Ms. McDow thought it was funny.

"Ha!" Pause.
"Ha!" Pause.
"Ha!" Pause.

"Green Eggs and Ham"

I loved the library at St. Joseph's because it had so many books.

I would get excited every time I had the chance to check out books to take home.

Green Eggs and Ham by Dr. Seuss was the first book I was able to read in English.

To tell you the truth, I was not able to read all the words, but I read some of them!

I didn't understand why the *huevos* were green, but I didn't care!

I was smart *en español* at home.

Now, I was learning to be smart in English at school!

6 A.M. Mass

Because St. Joseph's Elementary was not close to my *casa*,
my parents drove me to school every morning before
they went to sew pants at the factory.

The school cafeteria did not open until 7 a.m.,
but my parents had to be at work by 6:30 a.m.
So, I was dropped off at 6 a.m. mass to wait
until the school opened.

My *mamá* would get off the car and she would
walk with me into St. Joseph's Church,
all the way to the front and
she sat me on the first pew,
gave me a kiss on the forehead and told me,
"*Te queremos mucho*," and
reminded me to behave.

The priest was beautiful.
I loved his clothes. I wanted to dress like him.
And, he was nice.
And, he spoke English and *español*.
And, he told me that I was smart because I knew how to read in *español* and now I was
learning English.

He also told me that knowing two languages was a gift and that I should never be ashamed of my *mamá* and my *papá*, even if they only spoke *español* because they loved me and would do anything to make sure that I was happy.

My parents had talked to
him, and told him that they had to get to work
early, and that they would have to drop me off
at the first mass of the day.

The priest told my parents that he would
watch me and make sure that I got to the cafeteria after mass.

Six a.m. mass was one of my favorite parts of the day.
There were only a handful of people at church that early, but
they were always the most kind.

I was only six years old in first grade
and seven years old in second grade,
and 6 a.m. mass, and the priest, and
the strangers at mass made me
feel safe.

I learned English at mass because it was the language used by the priest.
I learned how to say the Our Father prayer.
I learned that I was a sinner, but that I could be forgiven in confession.

The priest also taught me that "In the name of the Father" was
the same as *"En el nombre del Padre"* and that I would be able to
serve our Lord in English and *español*.

I still remember his kind eyes.
The priest who loved English and *español*.
Six a.m. mass.

I was six years old in first grade, and
seven years old in second grade, and
I went to 6 a.m. mass *todos los días*.

Chico's Tacos

If you are from El Paso, you
know
Chico's Tacos!

The order of three rolled *taquitos*,
more like skinny *flautas*,
with a lot of cheese
that looks and tastes like the cheese that we got
from the government with our WIC coupons,
and that tastes so good,
and that also has a liquid
tomato sauce that
is almost clear and that
tastes very different than tomatoes,
but it is so good you really want a
double order that comes with six tacos, but
my *mamá* always said, *"estás loco"* and only
got me the single
because I could be a little crazy sometimes, and
because my *mamá* is funny and also, she
knows what is best for us.

People sometimes say that Chico's Tacos
is gross, but they don't understand
why they are so good, because they don't know about Fridays
at Memorial Park, right by the El Paso Zoo.

On Fridays, after I finished school at St. Joseph's, my parents
would take us to Memorial Park where the first Chico's Tacos is still located, and
my *papá* would play with us:
Frisbee, and kickball, and catch, and tag, and we would get on the swings too,
and my *mamá* would sit on a blanket watching us smiling after
we had eaten Chico's Tacos.

When I was five and six
at St. Joseph's, in first and second grade,
Chico's Tacos was the prize for learning to
speak English and staying in school.

Chico's Tacos is good and
I don't care what anyone says!

Return to Monte Vista Elementary School

Not every part of being at St. Joseph's was bad, and only half was bad, and
I am glad that I learned English even if I
had to be tied to a rolling bed, but I
also wanted to go back to Monte Vista because
my *mamá* and my *abuelita* Juanita kept telling
me that I was smarter than all
of the kids at the school because
I could read and write and speak in English and *español*,
and I decided that I didn't have to go to
6 a.m. mass anymore, and that I
could return to Monte Vista and
show them that they had kicked me out of kinder and first grade
for not speaking English, and for
kicking and crying, but that
I was not a bad kid, and that,
now, I was making As and
Bs, and that I was an *experto* in *español*,
even if no one cared because
I even knew where the accents went, because
my *mamá* taught me about words that were
agudas, and *esdrújulas*, and *sobresdrújulas* with
her special way of teaching, that meant she pinched me, but
not that hard, because she is a great teacher, and
when I finished practicing and learning in *español*,
I would lie on the couch with my head on her lap and
we would watch *telenovelas* together, especially my
favorite one that was
called

Los ricos también lloran,

with my favorite actress of all time, Verónica Castro.

And, that is when I returned to Monte Vista in third grade.

Back to School Night:
Part Three

I look at the families that I am charged to serve, and I feel blessed.

All roads and experiences have brought me here.

"Parents, *padres*, familes, our motto, *nuestro lema*, at this new school is *lo que se dice, se hace*. What you say, you do."

I tell them about my Abuelita Juanita and her *chancla*.

I tell them that my parents don't speak English even though they have been in the United States for forty years.

I tell them that they have an elementary education from Juárez and that they worked at Levi's and Farah, and also that my *papá* is now a janitor at a bilingual elementary school in El Paso.

I tell them about St. Joseph's and how I entered the school system tied to a rolling bed.

I tell them that the teachers that have been chosen to serve at this school WANT to be here and want to serve all families.

I tell them about the three goals of a dual language education.

I tell them about how I never dreamed that I would be a principal because as a kid, I had been ridiculed for speaking *español*, for being Mexican, for being short, for being fat, for not being White, and for not having a family with lots of money.

I tell them that at this school it doesn't matter if they speak English, or Spanish, or German, or Farsi.
They are welcomed and loved.

I tell them that we don't care if they are rich, or poor, or Black, or White, or Latino, or gay, or straight, or Muslim, or Catholic, or a doctor, or a factory worker.
They are welcomed and loved.

I tell them that it doesn't matter to us if students have traveled to Europe or have never been to the other side of the city.
They are welcomed and loved.

And, I tell them how I wished that my Abuelita Juanita was with us at this event so that she would know how important she has been in my becoming an educator.

I tell my parents and my family that I love them for always accepting me—all that I am, and also, all that I will never be.
I tell the school community that at this elementary school, we will all be family and that everyone has to know the motto that my *abuelita* had taught me so long ago.

I pull up a picture of Juanita on the screen. She is there, even if she is sick in Juárez. She is there because she is always with me. She is there because everyone in this space already knows her and loves her.

I tell them that if we are not people of our word, we have nothing.

I tell them that when I say, "Barron Bears, *lo que se dice,*" they will respond, "*Se hace.*"

I scream, "Barron Bears, *lo que se dice,*"

They yell, "*Se hace.*"

"Barron Bears, *lo que se dice...*"

"*Se hace.*"

"Barron Bears, *lo que se dice...*"

"*Se hace.*"

"Barron Bears, *lo que se dice...*"

"*Se hace.*"